GRADE

The 2007 & 2008 Syllabus should b[...] requirements, especially those for s[...] sight-reading. Attention should be [...] Notices, where warning is given of any changes.

The syllabus is obtainable online at www.abrsm.org, from music retailers or from the Services Department, The Associated Board of the Royal Schools of Music, 24 Portland Place, London W1B 1LU, United Kingdom (please send a stamped addressed C5 (162mm x 229mm) envelope).

In exam centres outside the UK, information and syllabuses may be obtained from the Local Representative.

CONTENTS

Where appropriate, pieces in this volume have been checked with original source material and edited as necessary for instructional purposes. Any editorial additions to the texts are given in small print, within square brackets, or – in the case of slurs and ties – in the form ⌒. Fingering, phrasing, pedalling, metronome marks and the editorial realization of ornaments (where given) are for guidance only; they are not comprehensive or obligatory.

Editor for the Associated Board: **Richard Jones**

Alternative pieces for this grade

Music origination by Barnes Music Engraving Ltd
Cover by Økvik Design
Printed in England by Headley Brothers Ltd,
The Invicta Press, Ashford, Kent

A:1 # Prelude and Fugue in A flat, BWV 862

No. 17 from *Das wohltemperirte Clavier*, Part I

J. S. BACH

Prelude
[♩ = *c*.84]

Reproduced from J. S. Bach: *The Well-Tempered Clavier*, Part I, edited by Richard Jones, with commentaries by Donald Francis Tovey (ABRSM Publishing)

Fugue

[♩ = *c*.60]

A:2

Prelude and Fugue in D

No. 2 from *Six Preludes and Fugues*, Op. 35

MENDELSSOHN

Adapted from Mendelssohn: *Six Preludes and Fugues*, Op. 35, edited by Howard Ferguson (ABRSM Publishing)

Fugue

Tranquillo e sempre legato [♩ = *c*.66]

A:3

Sonata in A minor

Kp. 175

D. SCARLATTI

Reproduced from Scarlatti: *Selected Keyboard Sonatas*, Book III, edited by Richard Jones (ABRSM Publishing)

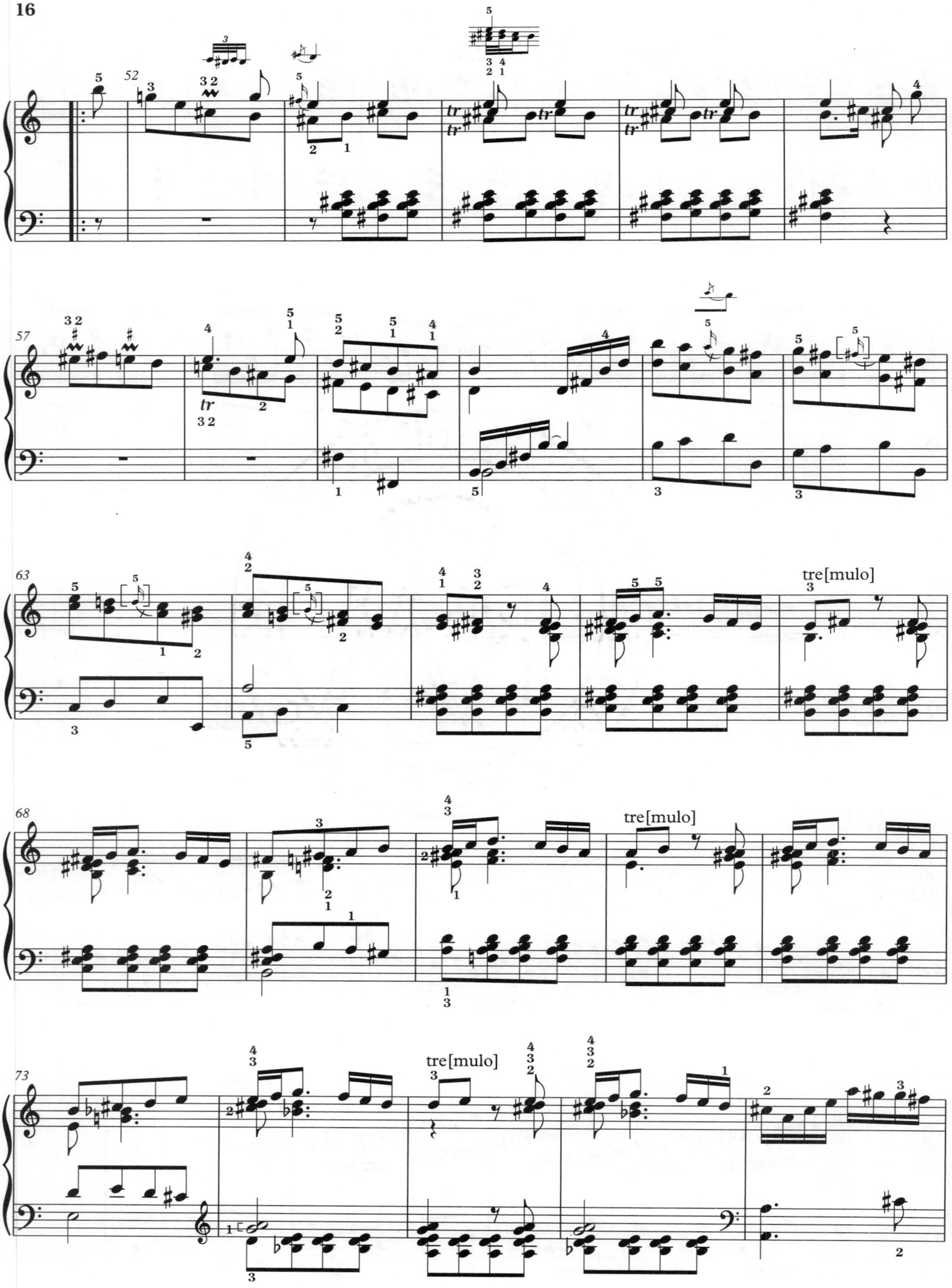
tre[mulo]
tre[mulo]
tre[mulo]
tre[mulo]

B:1

Allegro con spirito

First movement from Sonata in G minor, Op. 7 No. 3

CLEMENTI

Allegro

First movement from Sonata in E flat, Hob. XVI/52

HAYDN

B:2

B:3

Allegro

First movement from Sonata in F, K. 332

MOZART

Adapted from Mozart: *Sonatas for Pianoforte*, Vol. II, edited by Stanley Sadie and Denis Matthews (ABRSM Publishing)

feel crochet beat

new mood

C:1

If the Silver Bird could speak

ELEANOR ALBERGA

AB 3150

The Puppets' Dance

No. 5 from *Puppets*, Book 1

MARTINŮ

C:2

C:3

Gavotte

No. 2 from *Three Pieces from Cinderella*, Op. 95

PROKOFIEV

C:4

Mouvement de menuet

Second movement from *Sonatine*

RAVEL

Un peu plus lent qu'au début
[a little slower than at the beginning]

C:5

Vals romántico

No. 3 from *Linterna mágica*, Op. 101

TURINA

Tiempo de Vals (a 1, pero sin precipitar) [♩. = *c.*56]
[1 in a bar, but without rushing]

con sentimiento exaltado
[with an exalted feeling]

rubato y un poco libre [rubato and a little free]

Jazzy

No. 3 from *Three Moods*

COPLAND

Notes on the Pieces

A:1 J. S. Bach: Prelude and Fugue in A flat, BWV 862

Bach completed *Das wohltemperirte Clavier* (Part I), a set of 24 preludes and fugues in all keys, in 1722 when he was Kapellmeister to Prince Leopold of Anhalt-Cöthen. His purpose was not only to demonstrate a 'well-tempered' system of tuning that made it possible to play in all 24 keys, but also to encourage the study of keyboard and composition: according to the original title-page, the work was designed 'for the use and profit of the musical youth desirous of learning, as well as for the pastime of those already skilled in this study.'

For the tempo of the Prelude in A flat, Donald Francis Tovey recommends a 'cheerful *allegretto*'. The chordally accompanied ritornello theme (bb. 1, 18 and 35) and the flowing episode in double counterpoint (bb. 9 and 26) may be differentiated by contrasting touch and dynamics. For the Fugue, Tovey suggests 'Moderato, con moto tranquillo', adding: 'there is no room for anything but the broadest legato in the touch, unless a certain bell-like uniform detachment in the quavers be preferred.'
Source: autograph MS, Staatsbibliothek zu Berlin, Preussischer Kulturbesitz, Mus.ms.Bach P 415

A:2 Mendelssohn: Prelude and Fugue in D

The *Six Preludes and Fugues*, Op. 35, published in 1837, testify to Mendelssohn's lifelong veneration for the music of J. S. Bach, whose complex, highly expressive counterpoint fascinated and deeply influenced him. Mendelssohn integrates Bachian elements into his own personal style. Schumann wrote: 'the fugues have much of Sebastian [Bach] and could fool the sharpest critic, were it not for the song, the fine melting quality, in which one perceives the modern time, and here and there those small touches peculiar to Mendelssohn.'

According to Howard Ferguson, the tempo mark in the autograph sketch of the Prelude, *Andante quasi Allegretto*, suggests a speed on the slow side of *allegretto*. The LH quavers are best gently detached rather than sharply staccato (whether or not dots are marked); and pedal changes need to be frequent to avoid blurring the detached bass. The texture of the Fugue is legato throughout. The marking *dolce* in b. 53 implies *piano subito* after the preceding crescendo. The RH of bb. 59–60 is garbled in the source and has been emended by the editor.
Source: first edition, *Sechs Praeludien und Fugen* (Leipzig: Breitkopf & Härtel, 1837)

A:3 D. Scarlatti: Sonata in A minor

Most of Scarlatti's solo keyboard sonatas, which number nearly 600, were written after his move from his native Italy to Portugal (1719) and Spain (1728) as Master of the Chapel and music teacher to the young Princess Maria Barbara. Their boldly original style, characterized by Scarlatti himself as 'an ingenious jesting with art', often manifests itself in special colouristic effects of melody, harmony and rhythm. In the A minor Sonata, Kp. 175, these take the form of dissonant acciaccaturas – a note written as part of the chord, but foreign to the harmony and to be released the instant it is struck. Thus the LH of bb. 1–3 might be executed:

A similar mode of execution might be adopted in analogous contexts elsewhere.

The appoggiatura figure from the lyrical secondary theme (b. 17) is treated sequentially in bb. 25 ff., enhanced by richly dissonant harmony and melodic ornaments. The suggested interpretation is (*tremulo* in Scarlatti apparently signifies long or repeated mordents):

A melodically enhanced variant of this passage occurs in the middle section (upbeat to b. 66), which might be executed thus:

Source: Parma I (1752) 28

B:1 Clementi: Allegro con spirito

Muzio Clementi (1752–1832), an English pianist and composer of Italian birth, wrote about 100 keyboard sonatas, which are widely regarded as his most important works. During a continental tour as a solo pianist in the early 1780s he stayed in Vienna for six months (December 1781 to May 1782), taking part in a famous piano contest with Mozart and composing the 12 'Viennese' sonatas Opp. 7–10. 'Most impressive as an entire composition', according to Clementi's biographer Leon Plantinga, 'is surely the G minor Sonata Op. 7 No. 3. Its first movement presents extremely diverse musical materials that nonetheless achieve a complex motivic unity on several levels.'

The secondary theme in B flat major (b. 21) obviously calls for a new dynamic – perhaps *mf* or *mp*. The notation ♩ 𝅘𝅥𝅯𝅘𝅥𝅯𝅘𝅥𝅯 in bb. 85–6 etc. is a standard 18th-century shorthand for 𝅘𝅥𝅮𝅘𝅥𝅯𝅘𝅥𝅯𝅘𝅥𝅯
Source: first edition, *Trois sonates*, Op. 7 (Vienna, 1782)

B:2 Haydn: Allegro

The Sonata in E flat, Hob. XVI/52, one of the last of Haydn's 60-odd piano sonatas, was composed in 1794 during his second visit to London. It was dedicated to Therese Jansen, an outstanding pupil of Clementi and one of the most brilliant pianists of the day. A. Peter Brown (*Joseph Haydn's Keyboard Music*, Bloomington, 1986) describes it as 'a big sonata in every sense [which] requires power, dexterity and expression'. On the largest scale of all Haydn's sonatas, it forms the culmination of the Classical sonata while anticipating Beethoven.
Source: *A New Grand Sonata, for the Piano Forte*, Op. 78 (London: Longman, Clementi & Co., 1799)

B:3 Mozart: Allegro

The Sonata in F is the third of a set of three sonatas, K. 330–2, which were composed in the early 1780s, either in Munich or in Vienna. They have become some of Mozart's best-loved keyboard compositions. According to Denis Matthews, the spread chord in b. 25 may be read into b. 29 and parallel places later. Note that bb. 220–1 show how the LH crotchets of bb. 84–5 might be executed.
Sources: autograph MS, Scheide Library, Princeton, NJ, USA; first edition, *Trois sonates pour le clavecin ou pianoforte* (Vienna: Artaria, 1784)

C:1 Eleanor Alberga: If the Silver Bird could speak

Eleanor Alberga was born in Kingston, Jamaica in 1949. After moving to London in 1970, she trained as a pianist and singer at the Royal Academy of Music. She has sung with the celebrated Jamaican Folk Singers. The task of writing music for the London Contemporary Dance Theatre launched her career as a composer. *If the Silver Bird could speak* dates from 1995. In this piece, note that any accidental should only be applied to the stave in which it appears. The composer prefers that pedalling be used only where indicated.

C:2 Martinů: The Puppets' Dance

Bohuslav Martinů (1890–1959) is considered the most important Czech composer of the 20th century after Janáček. His three series of *Puppets*, comprising 14 pieces altogether, were written between 1912 and 1924. They reflect Martinů's interests in composing for the stage, and the established Czech tradition of puppet theatre. In an earlier edition of 'The Puppets' Dance', the first LH note in b. 18 is *db*; either a *db* or a *gb* will be acceptable in the exam.

C:3 Prokofiev: Gavotte

Sergey Prokofiev (1891–1953) became, alongside Shostakovich, one of the outstanding Russian composers of the Soviet Union. The *Three Pieces from Cinderella*, Op. 95, of 1942 were drawn from the ballet *Zolushka* (Cinderella), one of his most significant works of the Second World War period. The ballet includes several 18th-century dances – gavotte, passepied and bourrée – returning to the spirit of that age in a manner recalling the composer's well-known *Classical Symphony* of 1916–17.

C:4 Ravel: Mouvement de menuet

The French composer Maurice Ravel (1875–1937) was fond of recreating older styles of music and invigorating them with a more modern harmonic idiom. This propensity is illustrated in the *Sonatine* of 1903–5, which, according to Barbara L. Kelly (in *The New Grove Dictionary of Music and Musicians*, London, 2001), is 'Classical in character, not only in its use of sonata form and the minuet, but in its melodic clarity, regular phrasing and cadences.'

C:5 Turina: Vals romántico

The Spanish composer and pianist Joaquín Turina (1882–1949) studied in his home town of Seville, at the Madrid conservatory, and then in Paris, where he lived from 1905 to 1914. That year he returned to Madrid, where he was active as a teacher, composer, conductor and critic. Like his compatriots Falla and Albéniz, he incorporated Spanish folk idioms in his music. Of Turina's many works for his own instrument, the piano, *Linterna mágica* (Magic Lantern), Op. 101, is one of the last, dating from 1945.

C:6 Copland: Jazzy

Aaron Copland (1900–90), one of the outstanding American composers of the 20th century, took a strong interest in jazz from an early age and used it to help forge a distinctively American style of composition. His *Three Moods* date from 1920–1 and were first performed by Copland himself in Paris in September 1921. Just before the first performance, Copland wrote to his parents that No. 3 'is based on two jazz melodies and ought to make the old professors sit up and take notice.' A month later he visited the renowned composition teacher Nadia Boulanger, and it was on the strength of his performance of 'Jazzy' in her presence that she accepted him as a composition student. In the exam, a suitable tempo for the outer sections of this piece would be ♩ = *c*.76. Candidates may interpret the dotted-quaver, semiquaver figures as swung quavers, at their discretion.